AC/DC TRIVIA BOOK

Uncover The Epic History & Facts Every Fan Needs To Know!

By

Dale Raynes

Bridge Press

Support@BridgePress.org

Please consider writing a review!

Just visit: purplelink.org/review

ISBN: 978-1-955149-27-3

TABLE OF CONTENTS

INTRODUCTION

Many observers have described AC/DC as the greatest Rock 'n' Roll band of all time. They are, without a doubt, the most authentic rock band. In their fifty years of existence, AC/DC has shown an uncompromising commitment to the strong and relentless spirit of loud, defiant, irresistible, and straightforward rock.

They have refused to budge an inch from their sound, ignoring all fashions and passing trends. So you won't find any new-wave, techno, or hip-hop experimentation in their canon. These Australians have always stuck to what they do best: rock.

But don't mistake the immediacy of their songs for simplicity. AC/DC has overcome incredible challenges and moments of tragedy that would throw lesser bands into disarray, but nothing could stop Angus, Malcolm, and the boys. In the process of emerging as rock's ultimate survivors, AC/DC put together some of the most deadly riffs and catchiest songs in rock history. In the process, they have recorded the best-selling rock album in the history of the world.

There is more to their music and their story than you think. So get ready to delve into the High Voltage world of AC/DC if you dare.

CHAPTER 1:

THE EARLY DAYS OF AC/DC

1. Where was Angus Young born?

    a. Australia
    b. New Zealand
    c. The United Kingdom
    d. Canada

2. True or False: Malcolm and Angus had one other brother, and he was also a well-known musician in Australia.

3. Where was Bon Scott born?

    a. Australia
    b. New Zealand
    c. The United Kingdom
    d. Canada

4. What was Bon Scott's actual first name?

    a. David
    b. Ronald

c. Friedrich
d. Max

5. Before he began singing, what was the first instrument Bon Scott played?

   a. Trumpet
   b. Guitar
   c. Drums
   d. Recorder

6. At what age did Bon drop out of school?

   a. 13
   b. 15
   c. 17
   d. He graduated with excellent grades.

7. True or False: Angus lost his first guitar in a fire.

8. True or False: Bon Scott spent an unhappy period in the Australian army.

9. Bon was sentenced to juvenile detention for nine months. What was he charged with?

   a. Giving a false name to police
   b. Unlawful carnal knowledge
   c. Escaping legal custody

d. Stealing petrol

10. In 1974, Bon almost died. What accident did he miraculously survive?

    a. A car crash
    b. A motorboat sinking
    c. An overdose
    d. A motorcycle accident

11. How tall is Angus?

    a. 5′2″
    b. 5′1″
    c. 5′
    d. 4′9″

12. True or False: Malcolm and Angus used to fight over which of them would get to play lead guitar.

13. Which guitarist does Angus cite as his initial and most crucial inspiration?

    a. Jimi Hendrix
    b. B.B. King
    c. Chuck Berry
    d. Eric Clapton

14. True or False: Bon once sang a jingle for Coca-Cola.
15. True or False: Angus and Malcolm often drank in Australian bars when they were underage.
16. True or False: The older Young brother, George Young, was deeply unimpressed with AC/DC initially but agreed to produce their debut album anyway.
17. AC/DC played one of their first shows on New Year's Eve in 1973. What was the name of the club they played?
    a. Chess
    b. Chequers
    c. Dominoes
    d. Marbles
18. The band's first manager, Dennis Laughlin, was a singer who occasionally fronted the band. What was the name of the Australian band that made him famous?
    a. Tootsie Roll
    b. Sherbert
    c. Marmalade

d. The Custard Boys

19. True or False: In the band's early days, they sometimes played high schools.

20. Why did original manager Dennis Laughlin leave the band?

    a. The band had alcohol problems.
    b. They were late for shows.
    c. He didn't like their style.
    d. One of the members slept with his girlfriend.

ANSWERS

1. C- The United Kingdom. Glasgow, Scotland, to be precise. However, the family immigrated to Australia when Angus was eight years old. They were experiencing economic hardship in Scotland and decided to pursue new opportunities down under in 1963. Angus remembers that the Young Brothers were unhappy with the move at first: "We wanted to go home. But when we saw both our parents crying the night we arrived, we took strength from that to try and stick it out."

2. False. Well, the one brother part is wrong. The musician part is not. Malcolm and Angus had seven brothers. They also had a sister, Margaret. George Young was a member of several groups and had a couple of international hits with the duo Vanda & Young. Their best-known songs were "Friday on My Mind" and "Love Is in the Air." The success of George's first band served as an inspiration to his younger brothers and their musical aspirations. Malcolm recalls, "The band was formed in a migrant

hostel. Two of the guys came from Poland to Australia, others came from Liverpool and Yorkshire, and George from Glasgow. Within nine months, those five immigrants who arrived with nothing in their pocket were at number one in the charts."

3. C- The United Kingdom. Also in Scotland! So in a sense, AC/DC is a Scottish band as well as an Australian one. It is also worth noting that Bon Scott got his nickname in what was meant to be a truncated version of the expression "Bonnie Scotland."

4. B- Ronald. Full name Ronald Belford Scott.

5. D- Recorder. His first performance was a recorder recital at North Fremantle Town Hall. You can hear him play the recorder for one of his early bands, Fraternity. That is him playing the instrument on the song "Seasons of Change." He also played the bagpipes like any good Scottish boy.

6. B- 15. Bon was not very interested in school.

7. False. Angus still has his first guitar, a Gibson SG, to this day. He bought it in 1970 and played it. He says, "until it got wood rot because so much sweat and

water got into it. I've still got it, and it's still my favorite guitar of them all."

8. False. Scott tried to enlist, but the military rejected him as "socially maladjusted."

9. Trick question: all of the charges. Why settle for one when you can have all of them? A friend recalled, he was arrested "for carnal knowledge. Underage sex. That doesn't even exist anymore. Bon had front, but he wasn't an aggressive tearaway. Alcohol is what got to Bon."

10. D- A motorcycle accident. According to Scott's wife, Irene Thornton, the accident changed his voice forever. "I did feel that after he had the neck injury and broken collarbone and a cut in his throat, his voice didn't sound the same," Irene revealed. "He didn't seem to be able to do the same thing - he was doing a lot of melodic singing before, had a beautiful tone in his voice, but I don't think that (tone) was the voice he ended up with or that what he had (before) was the AC/DC voice everyone knows." His friends were not surprised by the accident. He took a devil-may-care attitude towards driving at the best of

times. When the accident occurred, he was also in a very angry mood. His friend remembered, "Bon had an argument with Bruce Howe [ex-Fraternity bassist]; Bon was pretty pissed and stormed off on his bike. Half an hour later, we heard he was in a coma. It was touch and go."

11. A- 5′2″. Angus topped Maxim's list of the 25 Greatest Short Dudes of All Time. If you are curious, Yoda came in 6th.

12. False. Their roles had always been clearly defined. Malcolm said, "I used to mess around a little bit with lead at the time but not much; Angus, he was just so much better, he just went for it, and it was brilliant. My place was sitting with rhythm, and I love rhythm. I've always loved it."

13. C- Chuck Berry. Angus explained, "the sound of Chuck Berry's guitar. It's everything rolled into one: it's blues, it's rock and roll, and it's got that hard edge to it. To me, that's pure rock 'n' roll. It's not clean - it's nasty."

14. True. His band, The Valentines, was fairly

commercial and was hired to sell the soda in Australia.

15. False. They were always too small and couldn't get away with it. Malcolm remembered, "Me and Angus are pretty small; You can drink in Australia at 17 in the bars, and most of our friends got tall and looked 17 and were in the bars when they were 15. Me and Angus couldn't make it, though. They knew we weren't 18, so we spent a lot of time from 15 to 18 in the bedroom playing guitar. You just did it every day. You learned to talk and walk and play guitar."

16. False. George was amazed at how good the band was, even though it was very different from the style of music he was famous for playing. The older sibling recalled, "All of a sudden, the kid brothers were still the kid brothers...but my God, they knew how to play. There was no sort of, 'Do they have it or don't they have it?' It was obvious that they had something."

17. B- Chequers. It was on that occasion that Angus unveiled his trademark schoolboy outfit. Original singer David Evans remembers, "It was New Year's

Eve, we got that gig, and we killed it, we absolutely killed it because everyone was drunk, but anyway. It was a great start to the band to be in the top nightspot absolutely chock full of people going crazy on New Year's Eve. We couldn't have had a better start."

18. B- Sherbert. The band was one of the most successful in the country at the time. Playing mostly pop-oriented songs, their biggest hits were "Summer Love" and "Howzat." However, Loughlin left before they enjoyed a fair amount of international success.

19. True. The band was willing to play anywhere. Even there. Malcolm says, "We used to do these high school matinees for lunchtime kids. And they were great; kids would respond. It was a little bit pantomime when you look back, but kids loved it." In particular, they loved Angus's schoolboy uniform schtick.

20. C- He didn't like their style. The band was heavily into glam rock at the time, and Loughlin was not a fan. If you check out early pictures of the band, they are decked out in glam regalia, aside from Angus, who looks exactly the same in his trademark schoolboy uniform. Bassist Mark Evans recalled,

"When I joined, they wanted me to wear a red satin suit. I said, 'If my mates see me, they'll punch the crap out of me!' Malcolm was keen on T.Rex and took us to see The Glitter Band. We all liked Slade. Later, we got more into Free and the Stones. Bon was nuts about Alex Harvey."

DID YOU KNOW

- Angus may be known for wearing a schoolboy uniform on stage, but he did not wear one often as a child. "I didn't go to school much. I was prize truant. When I went in, it was like, 'Welcome, Mr. Young! A year is a long holiday, you know?' The first day I went to that school, we all went to assembly, and the headmaster dragged all the boys who'd been caught smoking up on the stage in front of the whole school. Of course, Malcolm was one of them. I got into a lot of trouble when I was young. I wouldn't say I was a budding bank-robber or anything, but I was a bit of a juvenile delinquent."
- The term AC/DC was often used as slang to denote individuals with a bisexual orientation. Therefore, many people believed that the band's name was a knowing reference to that, especially considering that they started their career in the sexually androgynous age of glam rock. However, the name was a fairly innocent reference to the electrical abbreviation, which denotes an "alternating current/direct current"

power supply. Therefore, the band must have known that it was also a term used to denote a bisexual orientation. In addition, the name may have been a nod to their early days, which included many gigs at gay bars in Australia.

- Although the schoolboy costume that became the band's trademark was the brainchild of Angus's sister Margaret, it seems to be an integral part of the guitarist's identity. Malcolm observed, "It's not an act. He takes it on full. I don't think anyone could become that intense method acting. That's what people expect, and he does it. Even I don't know how he gets himself into that state."

CHAPTER 2:

AN AUSSIE BAR BAND MAKES GOOD

1. The iconic schoolboy uniform is not the first costume that Angus wore on stage. So what did he try out as an earlier gimmick?

    a. A superman costume
    b. A clown costume
    c. A Napoleon costume
    d. A gorilla costume

2. In what city did Angus play his first gig in the legendary schoolboy uniform?

    a. Melbourne
    b. Perth
    c. Sydney
    d. Brisbane

3. True or False: The band had to finance their debut single, "Can I Sit Next To You Girl."

4. True or False: Bon really wanted to join AC/DC and begged to audition for the band.
5. True or False: When Scott first joined the band, it took a while until he fit in because he was older.
6. True or False: Bon got the band over glam rock and into their trademark gritty hard rock.
7. Who was the song "She's Got Balls" written about?
    a. Bon Scott's mom
    b. Bon Scott's wife
    c. Bon Scott's sister
    d. Bon Scott's neighbor
8. Only one song on the original release of *High Voltage* featured their first drummer, Peter Clack. So on which song did he play?
    a. "Baby, Please Don't Go"
    b. "Little Lover"
    c. "Soul Stripper"
    d. "She's Got Balls"
9. As of 2021, AC/DC ranks were amongst the top ten best-selling artists of all time in the United States?

a. They do not rank in the top ten.
b. 9th
c. 7th
d. 5th

10. True or False: *Rolling Stone Magazine* referred to AC/DC as "the greatest rock and roll band of all time."

11. In 1974 the band landed a gig warming up for one of the biggest names in glam rock. So which legend did they accompany on the Australian leg of their tour?

    a. Lou Reed
    b. David Bowie
    c. T. Rex
    d. Elton John

12. True or False: AC/DC was banned from playing on the government-owned Australian Broadcasting Commission station when they were coming up.

13. Which AC/DC album did not feature the band's name with a high voltage indicator between the AC and DC parts of the band name?

    a. *Highway to Hell*

b. *Stiff Upper Lip*
c. *High Voltage*
d. *Dirty Deeds Done Dirt Cheap*

14. Australians have a colloquial way of referring to the band. So what do many fans from down under call AC/DC?

    a. Acca Dacca
    b. Dicey Icey
    c. Adey Dacey
    d. Fracka Dacca

15. True or False: Malcolm was a big Led Zeppelin fan and admitted he stole a few riffs from Jimmy Page.

16. One of the songs on *High Voltage* had been released as a single with original singer Dave Evans. Which song was it?

    a. "Love Song"
    b. "Little Lover"
    c. "Can I Sit Next To You Girl"
    d. "High Voltage"

17. Who had the idea of adding bagpipes to "It's A Long Way To The Top (If You Wanna Rock 'n' Roll)?"

a. Angus
b. Malcolm
c. George
d. Bonn

18. True or False: The band didn't write any of the material for *High Voltage* in advance. Instead, it was primarily done in the studio.

19. True or False: Before being hired as the singer for the band, Bon Scott worked as their driver.

20. The band was scheduled to play at the Sunbury Music Festival in 1975. However, a conflict with the headliner and their management led to the band being bumped. So which band had the problem with AC/DC?

    a. Black Sabbath
    b. Led Zeppelin
    c. Deep Purple
    d. Kiss

ANSWERS

1. D- A gorilla costume. Bassist Mark Evans remembers that "Early in my time with the band [1975], Angus had a gorilla suit and then wanted to have this Tarzan thing. And we've done gigs, and on P.A., Bon would have like a rope type, everybody's swinging from side to side on the P.A. boxes. Angus and Bon, they would just bounce off each other."

2. C- Sydney. It was an open-air festival at Victoria Park in April 1974. The show is a landmark in the history of the band. Angus says, "That was the most frightened I've ever been on stage, but thank God, I had no time to think. I just went straight out there. The crowd's first reaction to the shorts and stuff was like a bunch of fish at feeding time - all mouths open. I had just one thing on my mind: I didn't want to be a target for blokes throwing bottles. I thought if I stand still, I'm a target. So I never stopped moving. I reckoned if I stood still, I'd be dead."

3. False. The band had the backing of their brother George, and he helped them gain a record contract

with Albert Productions. Angus remembered, "What was good was that Ted [Albert] advanced us a lot of the money so as we could get out there and tour and backup the records. For him, it was a long-term investment, but it paid in the end. It all helped."

4. False. In interviews, the modest Bon pretended that he was fortunate to be invited to join. However, original drummer Peter Clack remembers it very differently: "Bon was in the crowd. We knew he was a fantastic singer, so Malcolm, who was the brains, said, I'm going to put it on Bon, maybe he'll be interested. There was an audition, and he invited Bon to join. Bon said, Piss off, I've got my wife, and I'm about to start a job. When we got back to Melbourne, Bon called up and said, OK, Malcolm, I'm in. It turned out his job was to paint this big rusty ship in the dock at Adelaide. He was on his way in the cold, looked at the ship, and said, Fuck this, I'm not doing this for a living, turned round, phoned Malcolm, and packed a suitcase."

5. False. Bon immediately hit it off with the other guys and the fans. Peter Clack recalls the immediate

electricity: "Bon was charismatic and a tremendous singer. He was an MC, a proper showman, and the music was ideal for that. He'd have Angus up on his shoulders playing these screaming solos, or he'd be up on the P.A. stack – whatever it took to give people a good time." Angus gives him credit for shaping the band: "I don't think there'd have been an AC/DC if it hadn't been for Bon. He molded the character of AC/DC."

6. True. Glam was very big at the time, and the band liked a lot of it and thought they could fit in by wearing flashy outfits. Bon didn't so much convince them not to play glam, as much as his style was not suitable for it. Malcolm recalls, "when Bon came into the picture six months later, we had the key to go straight to rock'n'roll because he could deliver it, and he had his own style. Bon influenced the band to go more into the rock'n'roll thing, which we'd always liked anyway."

7. B- Bon Scott's wife. Angus claims that his wife Irene complained that he Bon never wrote any songs

about her. The guitarist explained, "So he wrote 'She's Got Balls,' and she left him!"

8. A- "Baby, Please Don't Go."

9. B- 9th. Some of the acts they have outsold include Pink Floyd, the Rolling Stones, and Bruce Springsteen.

10. True. Sort of. The magazine would never give AC/DC that status. However, Rick Rubin wrote an essay on the band, declaring them the greatest rock band ever.

11. A- Lou Reed. The gigs came during Lou's Transformer glam era peak. Original singer Dave Evans was not very impressed with the condition of the legendary Velvet Underground singer at the time: "Lou Reed was pretty out of it. When he toured, it was a bad time for him. He was helped on the stage with a person on each arm. I thought that was just a stage act, but when we had breakfast in the mornings, he had a person on each arm just to get breakfast. Lou was not in good shape, and when he toured, we really couldn't have a conversation with him."

12. False. Indeed, the Australian Broadcasting Commission (ABC) played a significant part in their early success. They had a series of appearances on Molly Meldrum's show *Countdown*.

13. D- *Dirty Deeds Done Dirt Cheap*. At least on the international release. However, the Australian album cover had the good old-fashioned logo.

14. A- Acca Dacca. Some Australians call it that because they don't want to offend people of a bisexual orientation. However, for most, it is a way of expressing solidarity and ownership over the most successful Australian band in history.

15. False. Malcolm was not a fan. He told an interviewer, "me and Angus went to see Led Zeppelin once. We left after a couple of songs. Singer was a blond feller. Bit of a poser." Angus was not more subtle: "Led Zeppelin and all that have just been poor imitators of The Who and bands like that. That's when I reckon."

16. C- "Can I Sit Next To You Girl." The band re-recorded the song with the new singer Bon Scott.

17. C- George. The producing brother had the idea to add a nod to the family and its Scottish heritage. Malcolm explained, "so George said, why don't we try some pipes in with the lead solo? Like an answering thing. Bon actually could play flute, not bagpipes, so he got the canter from the bagpipe and played the melody, and then we did the drones separate and put it on, and it sounded fantastic."

18. True. Malcolm says that was the only way they knew how to record at the time. He explained, "'Live Wire' and 'It's A Long Way To The Top' came together almost immediately in the studio. When we played live in those days, we used to jam a lot on stage because we were so short of original material. We used to play 'Jumpin' Jack Flash' and put in 15 minutes of bullshit so we could fill up a 40-minute set. And the riffs for 'Live Wire' and 'It's A Long Way To The Top' came out of those jams. Back then, we never went into the studio with anything more than a riff. In fact, we thought a riff was a song. We really didn't know any better."

19. True. Or at least Bon said it was. He explained, "I used to work for an agency in South Australia, and I was the chauffeur, and I used to drive the band around. From the hotel to the gig and back to the hotel. And these guys were looking for a singer. And I said I can sing. So they give me a tryout, and I got the job." However, this is typical of Bon's modesty. He was a successful singer before joining AC/DC, scoring some big hits with more pop-oriented bands. However, at the time, he fell on hard times. Friend Peter Head explained, "Bon was desperate to make a few bucks. He'd do a few weeks of hard work but deliberately choose a job he wouldn't want to do for the rest of his life. He'd dig roads, paint boats, mow lawns. He worked at a fertilizer company, shoveling shit for 10 hours a day."

20. C- Deep Purple. The event's organizers brought over Deep Purple to Australia. There was a significant dispute involving a local union and the management of the British band. Therefore, the organizers thought Purple would cancel. They asked AC/DC to play to prevent a riot from breaking out. Angus recalls that as

the band prepared to go on, "all these cars, all these Rolls-Royces come pulling down. This was Deep Purple, and they'd decided that they were gonna go on. Everything was cool as far as we knew. Then, at the last minute, something happened ... somebody said somebody threw a punch at our manager - one of Deep Purple's tour guys. We were all bunched up in this caravan, changing. I remember we all came running out." The members of the two bands didn't fight each other directly. Angus says, "[W]e never got to play in the end. But the next day, that was all you read about: 'AC/DC in a brawl with Deep Purple.' In the end, it elevated us - more people came to see us!"

DID YOU KNOW

- A lot of bands are referred to as "bar bands," but no other internationally successful band embodies that term like AC/DC. They cut their teeth in some of the grittiest bars in Australia, and their music developed in accordance with their surroundings. Malcolm remembers that club owners told them to get people dancing so they would drink more. The rhythm guitarist explained, "That's how we cut our teeth, getting people hot and sweaty and drinking. As long as they were up dancing, we were doing our job. The more they dance, the more they drink. Everyone was really happy. Everywhere we played, we were getting offers for residencies." Angus remembers those early days as a bit less fun. The younger brother recalled, "Sometimes you finished with just two strings because there was no way they were going to put up with a couple of minutes of you fixing the guitar. I remember one night I said to the rest of the band that I'm not going out there. The police couldn't get in the place. Some madman was running around inside the hall with a meat cleaver, chopping into the people! And the front row was all bikers. You looked out, and it was just like murderers' row, and the look on their faces is like, send us the little guy in the shorts!"

- AC/DC have never been critical darlings, but they seem to revel in their position as a simple good-time party band, unlike many other bands in that position. Angus Young summed it up nicely, saying that "You don't go to the butcher for brain surgery." Playing in this style is the only thing that makes sense to these guys. Angus explains, "People have said we've hung around long enough! But some bands fade when they try to adapt to what's current. We play rock music. It's a little bit late for us to do a ballad. Rock is what we do best. Sometimes I'm asked if I want to play music other than AC/DC. Sure, at home, I play a little blues, but after five minutes, I'm like, 'sod this!' And I'm playing hard rock again."
- In an earlier interview, Angus said, "Look, there's not much seriousness in it. It's just rock'n'roll. Chew it up and spit it out. If you look at it this way, most

of the kids in the street talk like that. It's the language of the clubs that we heard when we started off in Australia, same when we came here, in places like the Marquee. Kids would be swearin' their heads off. They don't say, 'Turn it up…;' they say, 'FUCKING TURN IT UP!' We're as subtle as what they are."

- The band took their albums less seriously than most of their peers, who often wanted to make an artistic statement with their releases. However, to AC/DC, the main goal in the album was to introduce a few good songs the fans would like into their live repertoire. Malcolm said about 'Let There Be Rock,' "I suppose we were getting a bit more serious, and we wanted to get a rawer sound and cut out those commercial choruses like 'T.N.T.' We knew exactly what we wanted, which were three really strong live tracks to flesh out the set. 'Whole Lotta Rosie' was on that album, wasn't it? We knew it was going to be a sure-fire winner, and 'Bad Boy Boogie' and 'Let There Be Rock' were the other two we felt would go the distance on stage. Those three overshadow most of the other songs on the album and ended up in the live set for years after."

- *Highway to Hell* is yet another album about booze, rock, and women. However, American evangelicals decided the album was satanic and picketed AC/DC. Angus remembers being very surprised. "As soon as we called the album *Highway To Hell*, the American record company immediately went into a panic. With religious things, I thought everywhere was like Australia. There, they call them Bible-thumpers, and it's a limited species, very limited! Christianity was never a popular movement. It's that convict background! But in America, you had guys in bed sheets and placards with prayers on, picketing the gigs." The band was also accused of planting satanic messages in their songs. The guitarist thinks that is hilarious, "fucking hell; play it backwards? It says it right up front: *Highway to Hell*!"

CHAPTER 3:

DOING DIRTY DEEDS AND DOING THEM CHEAP

1. In its first appearance on a record, "Baby, Please Don't Go" was a single B-side. So what song was on the A-side?

    a. "Love Song (Oh Jene)"
    b. "The Jack"
    c. "Rock 'N' Roll Singer"
    d. "Live Wire"

2. When the band first performed the song "Baby, Please Don't Go" on Australian TV, they caused a sensation. Why?

    a. It was the first time Angus appeared in his schoolboy uniform.
    b. The band cursed on live TV.
    c. Bon was drunk.
    d. Bon dressed in drag.

3. True or False: The album cover for *High Voltage* includes actual letters to Scott from an angry club manager and a love letter to the singer.

4. Angus is known for mooning the audience on occasion. What inspired him to bare himself the first time he did it at Reading Festival in 1976?

    a. Angus was drunk.
    b. Angus wanted to distract them from the bad show he was having.
    c. Angus was wearing uncomfortable pants.
    d. Angus wanted the crowd to pay attention to the band.

5. What inspired the song "Dirty Deeds Done Dirt Cheap?"

    a. Someone Bon Scott met in his youth.
    b. One of the bands roadies
    c. A well-known movie
    d. A cartoon

6. What inspired the famous refrain from "For Those About to Rock (We Salute You)?"

    a. A pub song

b. A school song
c. A football chant
d. A hymn

7. True or False: Though not a punk rock band, AC/DC had a deep kinship with the punk rock movement because they shared a similar no-nonsense attitude.

8. Which Atlantic A&R person discovered AC/DC and signed them to the label?

    a. Phil Carson
    b. Ahmet Ertegun
    c. John Kalodner
    d. Jerry Greenberg

9. Atlantic signed AC/DC in 1976. How many albums did the band commit to recording for the label?

    a. Two
    b. Four
    c. Six
    d. Fifteen

10. True or False: Atlantic soon regretted the deal they had signed with AC/DC.

11. True or False: Mark Evans remains bitter about the way he was fired from the band.

12. True or False: Angus Young was charged with indecent exposure after mooning the audience at a Springfield, Illinois, show.

13. AC/DC's first tour of the UK was canceled after a member of one of the bands they were supposed to tour with died. What tragic death led to the cancellation of the tour?

    a. Paul Kossoff
    b. Tommy Bolin
    c. Keith Relf
    d. Marc Bolan

14. True or False: Although he is not a boastful person, Angus is known as quite the ladies' man.

15. True or False: Though you wouldn't know it from his music, Angus has very eclectic musical tastes and keeps up with the latest hip-hop.

    a. What brand of cigarettes does Angus smoke?
    b. Chesterfields
    c. Benson & Hedges

d. Marlboro

e. Lucky Strikes

16. When the band recorded *Highway to Hell,* Atlantic pressured the band to take Mutt Lange as producer. Why did they want him?

    a. They believed the previous albums sounded bad.

    b. He was cheap and available.

    c. They wanted the band played on the radio.

    d. To keep the band in line

17. True or False: The band had a jazz saxophonist member.

18. True or False: The band doesn't like any songs from the album *For Those About to Rock (We Salute You).*

19. True or False: Towards the end, Bon often missed practice and recording sessions due to his alcoholism.

ANSWERS

1. A- "Love Song (Oh Jene)." Needless to say, the explosive B-side garnered far more attention. Angus hates the song and said, "Who in their right mind would want this to go out?" But the B-side saved the day. The guitarist says, "We were very fortunate. We actually scored a hit from the B-side! That was the one saving grace of the song."

2. D- Bon dressed in drag. A friend of the band remembers, "As soon as his vocals are about to begin, he comes out from behind the drums dressed as a schoolgirl. And it was like a bomb went off in the joint; it was pandemonium, everybody broke out in laughter. Scott had a wonderful sense of humor."

3. False. The letters are there, but they are fake.

4. D- Angus wanted the crowd to pay attention to the band. The guitarist says, "some blonde girl walked real slow across the photo pit right in front of the stage, and thirty thousand eyes went with her. It was a real showstopper. Malcolm said to me, you gotta

do something to get the crowd's attention back! So, I dropped my trousers."

5. B- A school song. The Young brothers went to Glasgow's Milncroft Primary School. It no longer exists, but they never forget the school song. It went, "School that is set on the hill, WE SALUTE YOU!"

6. D- A cartoon. Malcolm explained, "It was Angus that came up with the song title. It was based on a cartoon character that had the phrase as his calling card."

7. False. Any similarities are utterly coincidental. Angus says, "we liked Chuck Berry. And Berry sang about cars, women, and party time. That to us was rock'n'roll. Punks were locked into selling anarchy, like a political thing. To be honest with you, the first time I heard the word anarchy, I had to get a dictionary to look up the fucker! I'm limited - meaning a limited education - so that wasn't communicating anything to me. We would get punks showing up and spitting, and when anyone [in the band] got hit by gob, we'd be in the audience

punching the shit out of them. It wasn't like we were punk, but the reputation of the band was there."

8. A- Phil Carson. Carson was so beloved by AC/DC that they jammed with him and thanked him in the liner notes for *Back in Black.* Carson was also associated with Led Zeppelin and toured with them extensively. When asked why he signed AC/DC, Carson gave the only answer that makes sense: "Simple answer? I thought that they were a great rock'n'roll band."

9. D- Fifteen. The label must have really believed in the band because that is unheard of. Phil Carson explained, "Normally, you would do a deal for four or five albums over a period of five years. But I thought: "These guys can sell records."

10. True. The first two albums did not do as well as hoped. However, today the deal is still considered one of the best pieces of business the label ever struck. Phil Carson wanted his boss, Jerry Greenberg, to be happy with the contract, so he got one hell of a deal. As Carson explained, "I thought I'd better make a deal that he can't possibly complain about. So I signed a deal for

twenty-five thousand dollars per album, one confirmed album per year, with options going forward. And the math on that is I signed a deal for twenty-five thousand dollars with AC/DC that gave us the rights to fifteen albums."

11. False. Evans has gotten over it long ago. His band Rose Tattoo didn't make the kind of money AC/DC did (very few bands have), but they are legends in their own right. Mark is philosophical about how things turned out: "I've got to tell you, I'm in a very, very fortunate position because I'm complaining about the way Rose Tattoo and AC/DC have been linked on together over the years – it just seems to be something that the way it's turned out these days, it just seems to be right the way it's turned out."

12. False. But it almost happened! After a show in the town on October 3, 1985, one of the concertgoers was offended that Angus showed his famous Australian cheeks on stage. Therefore, Evangeline Mendoza, a caseworker for the state Department of Children and Family Services, filed a report against Angus. The Assistant State's Attorney decided not to file charges.

He stated, "We had to decide whether what this guy did was a provable case; this doesn't have any bearing on the legality of any other incidents of mooning, though." Despite being offended, Mendoza stayed for the entire show.

13. A- Paul Kossoff. The incredible former Free lead guitarist was playing for Back Street Crawler and died of a pulmonary embolism. Angus was a huge fan of Free, and they were a significant influence on his sound.

14. False. Angus says, "I had a few wild nights over the years, but most of the time, everyone else was having them for me. Because of the schoolboy uniform, some women have tried to mother me - they think I'm cute because I'm so short. But playing has always been the thing for me. I never really looked beyond the next gig. In the early days, all my mates used to say to me, 'You must be meeting loads of girls...' Well yeah, I used to meet plenty of girls, but none of them used to want to go home with me. Some women would come up and make, er, bold

statements, but I don't know why. There's nothing sexy about a schoolboy, is there?"

15. False. Are you kidding? Angus says, "when I get in a car, the first thing that goes in is a Muddy Waters tape, even though I've played it four hundred times. I love that and Chuck Berry. Nowadays, everything sounds so nice - buzz-free, hiss-free. I like that hiss! I like to hear the valves on the amplifier warming up. It's pure energy." Malcolm also didn't keep up with the times music-wise. Asked what he listens to nowadays, the rhythm guitarist answered, "The Stones and The Who… and that's about it."

16. B- Benson & Hedges. Producer Mark Optiz says that sessions with AC/DC all start the same way: "As soon as Malcolm walked in, he would open a pack of Benson & Hedges cigarettes and throw everyone one while Angus would make a cup of tea."

17. C- They wanted the band played on the radio. AC/DC was known for their live act but didn't have any hit singles that would get airplay and shift units. Malcolm remembers, "Atlantic Records in America were unhappy because they couldn't get the band on

the radio, and they were desperate for us to come up with something more accessible. We'd had our own way for a few albums, so we figured, let's give them what they want and keep everyone happy. Back then, Mutt Lange was still an unknown – I think he'd just produced the Boomtown Rats before he came to us. Mutt seemed to know music, and he looked after the commercial side while we took care of the riffs, and somehow we managed to meet in the middle without sounding as though we'd compromised ourselves." However, Angus insisted that the last thing he wanted was for his songs to be played on the radio: "As far as radio stations go, you can turn on the radio, and you wouldn't like to hear your songs on the radio anyhow, cos it's in there with Barry White playing his Love Unlimited bollocks. That's a bit degradin' for us."

18. True. Their first bassist was Larry Van Kriedt, a US-born musician who was also a jazz saxophonist. His father, David van Kriedt, had produced and arranged legends such as Dave Brubeck. Unfortunately, Larry

can no longer play the saxophone because he had cancer-related surgery on his jaw.

19. Almost true. They are not fans of that album. Malcolm said, "Christ! It took us forever to make that record, and it sounds like it. It's full of bits and pieces, and it doesn't flow properly like an AC/DC album should. There's some good riffs on there, but there's only one song we like, and that's the title track. By the time we'd completed the album, it had taken so long; I don't think anyone, neither the band nor the producer, could tell whether it sounded right or wrong. Everyone was fed up with the whole record."

20. False. Bon was a professional. "Bon would be the first one up in the morning, no matter what state he went to bed in. You'd get a cup of coffee by your bed. He would say, come on, time to get up and get into practice. He was driving us on a lot." Angus agrees, "Sometimes he'd get stuck, and he'd go down to a club for the night and get wasted, but, as Mal said, he was there first thing in the morning, putting these lyrics together."

DID YOU KNOW?

- Bon Scott has a reputation for being a hell-raising alcoholic. However, he was also a great guy. By all accounts, he was a good person and a reliable friend. Former drummer Peter Clack said, "He was a fantastic guy, a real human, so different to what people thought." A member of Bon's first band, Murray Gracie, explained that the singer was "a very respectful son. His parents came to a lot of shows, and we'd rehearse at their house." Another friend says that no matter how bad Scott's drinking got, he was never violent or mean: "He drank heaps. He drank until he could barely stand. But he always remained the same person." One of his ex-girlfriends, who prefers to remain anonymous (she is called Holly X in books and articles), said, "I haven't read a lot that's been written about Bon, but everything I have read it's all about his addiction and him getting high and stories about him being wasted and all this, and that was part of it, but he was a really, really neat guy. I cared a lot about him.

He was a lot of fun. He was a gentle person, gentle soul, in spirit, and very, very sensitive." Angus summed it up best, saying, "We all miss him terribly. It's rare that you come across someone in your life with such a big character. He'll always be with you."

- Kiss singer and bassist Gene Simmons is a huge fan of AC/DC. So he invited them to open for Kiss in their 1977 Tour. "There were lots of bands who played good rock'n'roll," Simmons recalls. "What struck me was this little lead guitarist who kept moving on stage like a wild man from Borneo, even between the blackouts. I was awestruck." Following the show, Gene Simmons entreated the budding guitarist to a late meal on Sunset Boulevard at Ben Frank's. "Angus ordered a hotdog and beans," Simmons says. "And I remember he picked up the hotdog in his hand, minus the bun, and put it in his mouth sideways because he had missing teeth. Here was a band to be reckoned with." He also loved Bon Scott. Gene summed up Bon's appeal, "maybe because he came from a hard background; he was the antithesis of the pretty-boy lead singers of the time. Shirtless. Hard singing. Hard-drinking. The voice was undeniable."

- The band is often criticized for writing simplistic songs. However, to the members, it is not a limitation. The basic structure is an ideology. Malcolm explained the vision behind the seemingly primitive approach of the band, "We were sitting on three chords, mainly. If there was a fourth chord, it was a bonus. But it was down to how you broke it up and arranged things, and with Bon's lyrics working within that. Within a couple of days in the studio, we pretty much had our thing locked in, and we all knew what we were doing. We kept everything simple. Most of the best songs ever written are three chords. That's the reality of it. We'd just go for the throat. That's what our whole thing was." The simplicity is a reflection of the band's upbringing and values. Malcolm said, "Nobody in this band gets aloof. It just keeps things in place, and it just keeps you, working-class people. We all have those traits, and that's kept us in the real world. You've got to go on and deliver every night; you've just got to do it, no matter what. Give it your best all the time. That's it, really."

- Today AC/DC are headliners. However, back when they were coming up, the band often opened for others. They were so good that no one wanted to follow them on stage. Guitar legend Eddie Van Halen remembers being quite intimidated: "I was standing on the side of the stage thinking, we have to follow these motherfuckers?" Another fabulous guitarist, Gary Moore of Thin Lizzy, had a similar experience: "In Cleveland, they blew us off the stage, fucking killed us."

CHAPTER 4:

HIGHWAY TO HELL

1. True or False: While Bon had been professional before, you could tell drinking and drugs were overcoming Bonn during the *Highway to Hell* sessions.

2. True or False: *Highway to Hell* was the first AC/DC album to make the top ten in both the US and the UK.

3. True or False: George Young was against hiring an outsider to produce *Highway to Hell.*

4. Which legendary producer started the *Highway to Hell* sessions with the band before being replaced by Mutt Lange?

    a. Alan Parsons
    b. Eddie Kramer
    c. Todd Rundgren
    d. Roy Thomas Baker

5. Where did the failed sessions with the first producer take place?
    a. Miami
    b. Las Vegas
    c. Atlantic City
    d. Reno
6. True or False: Angus immediately appreciated what Mutt Lange brought to the table.
7. Which member of the band did Atlantic want to replace to sell more records?
    a. Bon
    b. Angus
    c. Malcolm
    d. Phil
8. While recording the album, the band replaced their manager, Michael Browning, with a big-time American manager. Who was the new manager?
    a. Danny Fields
    b. Albert Grossman
    c. Peter Mensch
    d. Jon Landau

9. Bon quotes a line from a '70s sitcom on the album. Which show did he pay tribute to?

   a. *All in the Family*
   b. *Three's Company*
   c. *The Facts of Life*
   d. *Mork & Mindy*

10. How long did it take to record Highway to Hell?

   a. A month
   b. Two months
   c. Three months
   d. Four months

11. The tape of the original recording of the song "Highway to Hell" was almost destroyed. What destructive force almost deprived us of that magical riff?

   a. A dog
   b. A child
   c. Rain
   d. Faulty electricity

12. The band has been accused of copying the riff from the song "Beating Around the Bush." Which band played a very similar riff about a decade earlier?

    a. Cream
    b. Fleetwood Mac
    c. The Rolling Stones
    d. Led Zeppelin

13. True or False: In pursuit of a new sound for the band, Mutt Lange stopped them from recording live in the studio as they were used to.

14. Not long before Bon Scott passed away, AC/DC played Top of the Pops. Which song did they play?

    a. "Highway to Hell"
    b. "Touch Too Much"
    c. "Shot Down in Flames"
    d. "Walk All Over You"

15. Despite the success of *Highway to Hell,* Angus believes one of the songs on the album is terrible. So what song does the guitarist hate?

    a. "Girls Got Rhythm"
    b. "Beating Around the Bush"

c. "Love Hungry Man"
d. "Walk All Over You"

16. True or False: Atlantic liked the name *Highway to Hell* because they hoped the controversy would help sell records.

17. Where did Bon Scott die?

    a. London
    b. Sydney
    c. New York
    d. Paris

18. Which of the early AC/DC albums was not released by Atlantic in the US until after Bon Scott died?

    a. *High Voltage*
    b. *T.N.T*
    c. *Dirty Deeds Done Dirt Cheap*
    d. *Powerage*

19. The song "Night Prowler" was later associated with a serial killer. Who was the monster in question?

    a. Richard Ramirez
    b. Larry Eyler
    c. Joseph Christopher

d. Lonnie David Franklin

20. Which song ends with a delightful cackle from Bon Scott?

    a. "Highway to Hell"
    b. "Shot Down in Flames"
    c. "Walk All Over You"
    d. "If You Want Blood (You've Got It)"

ANSWERS

1. False. Bon was incredibly productive in the sessions. Tony Platt, who mixed the album, remembers, "The record was made on tea. The first time I met them, Bon made me a cup of tea. He was superb. When he sang, you believed him. The Youngs ran the band, but Bon was allowed to plough his own furrow. There were stories about him disappearing at the end of one gig and reappearing just in time for the soundcheck at the next. Malcolm once told me, 'The thing with Bon is, it doesn't matter what he does, he always turns up.' You got the impression he was resilient."

2. False. While it reached #8 in the US, *Highway to Hell* failed to crack the Billboard top 10. Instead, it peaked at #17.

3. False. Atlantic Records convinced the older brother that if the band was going to succeed in the US truly, it needed to go in a different direction. To George, the band was a raw rock band, and he didn't want to make them too commercial. He recalls, "It was always more important whether it had the balls. So, if we had

to choose a take where it was buzzing and all that, we'd go for that." Instead, it was Malcolm and Angus who were against replacing their brother. They saw the move as a betrayal. Their manager Michael Browning recalls, "George and Harry were pretty honorable about it. They could have been outwardly sort of pissed off. I'm sure they were. For an American record company to say you've got to change producers when they're sort of revered in their own country was a little bit of a slap in the face, I suppose. So it was very, very difficult. Malcolm and Angus didn't like it at all. They were very pissed off."

4. B- Eddie Kramer. Eddie had produced some of the most fantastic music of the late '60s and early '70s. From Jimi Hendrix to Kiss, he was behind some massive hits. But there was a real lack of chemistry. Kramer explains, "I think more than anything, the band resented me being foisted onto them. It was like sticking a pin into them." The final straw was when Eddie asked them to record a version of the Spencer Davis Group's "Gimme Some Loving." Years later, Kramer said, "I don't remember making

that suggestion. But if I did, what a dumb thing to say."

5. A- Miami, at Criteria Recording Studios. It is one of the most prestigious studios in America, where the Allman Brothers and Bob Seger recorded some of their best-known material.

6. False. Angus had no idea who Mutt was and did not trust his micro-management style at all. So when Lange tried to show Bonn how to sing a part, Scott snapped, "If you're so fucking good, you do it!" Lange then proceeded to sing it quickly without getting out of his chair. He slowly earned the respect of the band. Angus remembers why they were nervous, "We were very cagey about working with *anyone* new. At one point, we thought, Is there someone out there, other than George and Harry, who can really do justice to our music? You'd hear about producers taking a band away for two years, putting 'em in some mansion. And that was something we didn't want. So we were pretty nervous."

7. A- Bon. The record company began to feel that his voice was unintelligible, and he didn't have the kind of pretty boy image they expected from a lead singer.
8. C- Peter Mensch. Peter was an accountant for Scorpions and Aerosmith. But somehow, he persuaded AC/DC to make him their manager. He would later manage Metallica as well.
9. D- Mork & Mindy. At the end of the song "Night Prowler," you can hear Scott say, "Shazbot! Nanu nanu!" Those were the catchphrases of the alien character played by Robin Williams in the hit show.
10. C- Three months. It was a far cry from the quick romps of their early albums. The difference was Mutt Lange's perfectionism. Malcolm remembers that Mutt "liked the simplicity of a band. We were all minimalist. We felt it was the best way to be ... He knew we were all dedicated so he sort of got it. But he made sure the tracks were solid, and he could hear if a snare just went off."
11. B- A child. Angus remembers, "We were in Miami, and we were flat broke. Malcolm and I were playing

guitars in a rehearsal studio, and I said, "I think I have a good idea for an intro," which was the beginning of "Highway to Hell." And he hopped on a drum kit, and he banged out the beat for me. There was a guy in there working with us, and he took the cassette we had it on home and gave it to his kid, and his kid unraveled it. Bon was good at fixing broken cassettes, and he pasted it back together. So at least we didn't lose the tune."

12. B- Fleetwood Mac. The song in question is the classic "Oh Well," written by Peter Green. Some noted that it also serves as an inspiration to Led Zeppelin's "Black Dog" riff.

13. False. Mutt realized there was no other way to capture the band's raucous sound but live in the studio. Malcolm recalls, "Mutt realized that we were a good band who could play their instruments, so he just let us go for it. The freedom was there. And we gave him freedom as well – we would try anything he asked of us. Mutt fit in really well with the band."

14. B- "Touch Too Much." They also played "Rock 'N' Roll Damnation." It was one of Bon Scott's last performances with the band.

15. C- "Love Hungry Man." Angus said, "there's a song on *Highway to Hell* called 'Love Hungry Man,' which I must have written after a night of bad pizza - you can blame me for that."

16. False. They were very concerned about the backlash, which did indeed come.

17. A- London. Mutt Lange moved the band to London to finish the album in an atmosphere that suited them more. Unfortunately, it would also prove to be Bon's undoing.

18. C- *Dirty Deeds Done Dirt Cheap.* In fact, when they heard the tapes, Atlantic almost dropped the band. Phil Carson, who had signed AC/DC, remembered, "I went to Atlantic Executive Neshui Ertugen and showed him the sales figures that we'd got for *High Voltage*. They were not awe-inspiring but, considering we'd only paid $25,000 for the album. This was not so bad... Nesuhi backed me up, and I re-signed the band

at that point. I managed to claw it back in. Thank God." As for the release of the album after Bon's death, Carson said it was "one of the most crass decisions ever made by a record-company executive."

19. A- Richard Ramirez. He was a fan of AC/DC and particularly loved that song. Ramirez even left an AC/DC hat at the scene of one of the murders. However, the band insists the song has nothing to do with murders and is about a boy sneaking into his girlfriend's room late at night.

20. B- "Shot Down in Flames." The song is an excellent example of what set Bon apart from other frontmen of his generation. He wrote songs about self-deprecating experiences like getting rejected.

DID YOU KNOW?

- Many rock stars who die from substance abuse do so because they cannot deal with fame and the pressure that comes with it. However, Bon Scott did not have that problem. Mark Evans says that it was quite the contrary: "A lot of musicians are arrogant and negative; Bon didn't have an ounce of that. He was well-equipped to handle fame. He should have gone on for a long time." Mark Evans agrees, "Everyone loved him. He was a gentleman, fun-loving, great to be around. The public persona was this crazy guy, but that was only part of it. What hastened his departure is that he felt a responsibility to be Bon Scott, to live the rock'n'roll lifestyle he sang about."
- The official cause of Bon's death is "death by misadventure." This elegant British phrase refers to any preventable death, in this case, alcohol poisoning. However, some people with inside knowledge doubt that alcohol was the actual cause. One witness claimed, "It was a great party, and Bon

and I both drank far too much, both at the free bar backstage and at the upstairs bar as well; however, I did not see him take any drugs that evening." However, a close friend disputes this: "Bon was sober… I cannot remember Bon being drunk enough to kill himself in a car. I mean, come on." Bill Duffy, the future guitarist of the British band The Cult, drove Bon home after the party. Bill remembers, "At the end of the party, I offered to drive him home. As we approached his flat, I realized that Bon had drifted into unconsciousness. I left him in my car and rang his doorbell, but his current live-in girlfriend didn't answer. I took Bon's keys and let myself into the flat, but no one was at home. I was unable to wake Bon, so I rang Silver for advice. She said that he passed out quite frequently and that it was best just to leave him to sleep it off." Somehow, Scott ended up in a car where his body was found. There has been some speculation that he died in someone's home, and they removed his body to avoid getting into trouble. His friend Paul Chapman said, "somebody must have been extremely out of it upstairs, wherever upstairs was, and forgotten Bon was in the car. I remember how cold it was at my flat when the Calor gas went out, let alone being in a car outside. Whoever was down there with Bon in [East] Dulwich must have been upstairs nodding out. That's the only thing I can think of. I cannot believe that somebody would not go out and check on him in that weather."

- Since Bon was an experienced drinker, there is a theory that he died from heroin use. It appears that the people Scott was with that night were known, heroin users. Scott, meanwhile, was not used to the stuff. One woman who was there recently told an interviewer that there is good reason to believe that heroin was involved: "I didn't see him taking heroin, but both Alistair and Silver were users at the time. I would think it probable that [Bon] did take heroin as I would not have thought somebody that was used to drinking would have been sick. It's well known that if you take heroin when you have been drinking, especially if you don't normally, it could lead to you vomiting, plus cause you to pass out. But I can only presume that's what caused him to fall asleep and later vomit. He didn't seem unreasonably intoxicated. If he had taken heroin, it was with Silver and Alistair at the venue; I didn't see him [take heroin]. Unfortunately, the only persons that can know for sure are Silver and Alistair. I know how devastated Alistair was and how it affected him for years afterwards. It is so bad that we will never know what happened to Alistair. He was such a lovely guy, and his disappearance has left an unsettling feeling. I miss him." No matter what the cause, Bon's death was avoidable and, therefore, utterly tragic.

- *Highway to Hell* had a massive influence on the development of hard rock and heavy metal. Charlie Benante from trailblazing thrash metal band Anthrax recalls, "I didn't know too much about the band at the time; they weren't featured in magazines like other bands were, so you had to really dig to find out anything about AC/DC. *Highway To Hell* became a classic, especially with its having been Bon's final record with the band; it was such an awesome send-off even though no one knew it at the time. *Highway to Hell* is just classic AC/DC, everything about it, the production, the musicianship, it was their first record with Mutt Lang producing, it's just awesome, love it." Guitarist Slash from Gun N' Roses says that Angus is his all-time rock guitar hero because of the performance on that album. The top-hatted guitarist says, "I'll go with Angus Young at this point because he's somebody I've known for a really long time, and the first record I really heard from AC/DC was 'Highway to Hell.' I didn't hear any of the stuff prior to that, but that had a big enough of an impact, and then after that, 'Back in Black.' And then I got to meet Angus and Brian and the rest of the guys when I was opening for AC/DC with Snakepit in 2001. And they were just really great; they took me out on the road, took me under their wing; I just always loved their work ethic, always loved Angus's guitar style."

- The band considered breaking up after Bon's passing. The Young brothers felt he was too important to the band ever to be adequately replaced. Angus still has trouble talking about it. He remembers, "on the plane back; the management was going, All right, you guys, we've got some singers. We were like, his body isn't even cold yet, you bastards!'" Meanwhile, Malcolm says, "we didn't know what we were going to do. We were still really low. It took us about six weeks to get the band back together again. Me and Angus would ring each other every day, and we weren't snapping out of it." However, they knew Bonn would want them to carry on. In addition, the singer's family asked them to continue in his honor.

CHAPTER 5:

BACK IN BLACK

1. True or False: Bon Scott was a big fan of his eventual replacement, Brian Johnson.

2. Which AC/DC song did Brian Johnson sing in his audition for the bend?

   a. "High Voltage"
   b. "Let There Be Rock"
   c. "Whole Lotta Rosie"
   d. "Dirty Deeds Done Dirt Cheap"

3. In which Caribbean islands did the band record Back in Black?

   a. Trinidad & Tobago
   b. The Bahamas
   c. Bermuda
   d. Barbados

4. How long did the recording of *Back in Black* take?

   a. Four weeks

b. Five weeks
c. Eight weeks
d. Ten weeks

5. The bells tolling in "Hells Bells" are among the most famous moments in hard rock history. Who had the idea of including them in the recording?

    a. Angus
    b. Brian
    c. Mutt
    d. Malcolm

6. True or False: Atlantic Records hated the idea of a black cover for the album.

7. True or False: Rolling Stone did not recognize the album's brilliance and panned *Back in Black* in its original review.

8. The band recorded music videos for a few of the songs on the album. Where did they record them?

    a. The Netherlands
    b. Denmark
    c. Sweden
    d. Switzerland

9. *Back in Black* was a massive hit worldwide. In which country did it fail to reach #1.

    a. The United Kingdom
    b. France
    c. The United States
    d. Australia

10. How many albums have sold more copies globally than *Back in Black*?

    a. None
    b. One
    c. Five
    d. Eight

11. Which of these songs did Bon write and record a demo of not long before his untimely death?

    a. "Hells Bells"
    b. "Let Me Put My Love Into You"
    c. "Shake a Leg"
    d. "You Shook Me All Night Long"

12. True or False: Brian was a natural in the studio and did not require much coaching from Mutt or the band.

13. During the recordings, a session was interrupted by which aquatic creature?

    a. A pelican
    b. A crab
    c. A sea turtle
    d. An isopod

14. One of the songs on the album has been played in more strip clubs than any other song in history. Which song has accompanied the most pole dances?

    a. "You Shook Me All Night Long"
    b. "Back in Black"
    c. "Hells Bells"
    d. "Shoot to Thrill"

15. Which song on the album helped reassure a Marine in captivity that he would be released?

    a. "You Shook Me All Night Long"
    b. "Back in Black"
    c. "Hells Bells"
    d. "Shoot to Thrill"

16. What type of booze is NOT referenced in the song "Have a Drink On Me?"

a. Whisky
b. Gin
c. Vodka
d. Brandy

17. True or False: Bon Scott wrote the lyrics to "You Shook Me All Night Long."

18. What is the song "Shoot to Thrill" about?

    a. A prostitute
    b. A hitman
    c. A drug dealer
    d. A soccer player

19. True or False: AC/DC does not allow sampling and has taken action against hip-hop acts for sampling the legendary *Back in Black* album.

20. Most people can agree that "Back in Black" is one of the greatest hard rock songs. So, where did VH1 rank it in their "100 Greatest Hard Rock Songs" chart?

    a. First
    b. Second
    c. Third

d. Fourth

ANSWERS

1. True. Brian remembers that Bon saw him sing when he was suffering from acute appendicitis: "I met Bon in 1973 or 1974. His band was supporting my band, GEORDIE. I had a terrible case of appendicitis, and I went down on my side, kicking and going, 'Ooh!' But I kept on singing." Bon thought that his kicking and screaming in pain was an act and loved the show. He was also inspired to hoist Angus on his shoulders after seeing Brian do it with the guitarist from his band Geordie. Brian was so impressed. He told the rest of the band that they should bring Johnson into the band if anything ever happened to him. Angus remembers, "Bon had been in a band that had toured in Britain, and they were opening for the band Brian was in, which was a band called Geordie. Anyhow, they were gigging away, and as Bon told the story, he was saying he was listening to Geordie performing and listening to Brian, and then he heard this screaming. He said it sounded great – he said it sounded like Little Richard was on the stage. He said

this guy [was] howling and yelling. And then he said then he saw the guy on the floor. Bon thought it was great – it was the best act he had seen, and a singer, in a long time." This was a big deal. Angus notes that "It was rare that Bon ever raved about anything." Therefore, it was clear that Brian was the right choice.

2. C- "Whole Lotta Rosie." He also did the Ike and Tina Turner classic "Nutbush City Limits." What impressed the band the most was just how loud the singer was. Malcolm remembers, "we wanted to check how powerful he was. Could he get above the band? He was the first singer we heard for real; you could actually *hear* him. We thought he's got the tools, big chest."

3. B- The Bahamas. They recorded it on the island of Nassau at Compass Point Studios.

4. B- Five weeks. Surprisingly, *Back in Black* took a fraction of the time of its predecessor. *Back in Black* sounds far more polished than *Highway to Hell.*

5. D- Malcolm. The rhythm guitarist had a flash of inspiration while recording the song at Electric Ladyland Studios in New York.

6. True. After all, this was the disco era. So they tried a variety of different cover suggestions. Angus explained, "We knew what we were going to call the album because it was our thing for Bon - Back in Black. We all knew that. And we wanted [the sleeve] in black. You try convincing the record company when the front guy's passed away that you want an album called Back in Black with a black sleeve." Malcolm added that, "the record company sent you a pink jacket for it. We'd sent the album cover back six times each week, and [we said] black, with nothing on it. We want it embossed, so you don't need white lines on it. All without pictures. We settled in the end for a slight grey liner, so we managed to get virtually what we wanted."

7. False. For a change, *Rolling Stone* immediately recognized the classic. Writer David Fricke declared that it was "not only the best of AC/DC's six American albums, it's the apex of heavy metal art:

the first LP since *Led Zeppelin II* that captures all the blood, sweat, and arrogance of the genre. In other words, *Back in Black* kicks like a mutha." *The Observer*, meanwhile, featured what might be the wordiest review for a basic three chords hard rock album imaginable: "a preposterous, drongoid record ... built on casual sexism, eye-rolling double entendres, a highly questionable attitude to sexual consent ('Don't you struggle/ Don't you fight/ Don't you worry/ Cos it's your turn tonight') a penchant for firearms, and a crass celebration of the unthinking macho hedonism that killed the band's original singer."

8. A- The Netherlands. In the days before MTV, there were no real mediums to play music videos. However, Atlantic believed (correctly) that they would be needed to market albums in the future. So, AC/DC spent an afternoon in the city of Breda, recording videos for "Hells Bells," "Back in Black," "What Do You Do For The Money Honey," and "Rock'n'Roll Ain't Noise Pollution," among other songs. But just because they were doing it for a video

didn't mean the band didn't play with their usual volume. Malcolm recalls, "That was a real quick job. The camera crew were holding their ears, and they went on strike. We were too noisy. They all put on their airplane muffs, and they were still complaining."

9. C- The United States. In America, it only reached #4. However, it went on to sell 25 million copies in the States.
10. B- One. That album is Michael Jackson's *Thriller. Back in Black* has sold over 50 million copies, making it the highest-selling hard rock (or any kind of rock really) album of all time.
11. B- "Let Me Put My Love Into You."
12. False. Mutt is an accomplished singer and a known perfectionist when it comes to vocals. But, by all accounts, he pushed Brian to the breaking point during the sessions. The singer recalls, "He wouldn't let anything go past him. He had this thing where he didn't want people to listen to the album down the road and say there's no way someone could sing that,

they've dropped that in, even the breaths had to be in the right place. And you cannot knock a man for that, but he drove me nuts."

13. B- A crab. The little creature had wandered into the studio, which was not sufficiently insulated. In addition, sea birds kept flying away and making noise whenever they tried to use the "Hells Bells" bell.

14. A- "You Shook Me All Night Long." Yes, there are strip club charts, and they are called the Panda Charts. But, no, we don't know why. Other highly popular strip club songs include Def Leppard's "Pour Some Sugar On Me" and the Nine Inch Nails' song "Closer."

15. C- "Hells Bells." Mike Durant was behind enemy lines after his helicopter had been shot down on a mission in Somalia. If you ever saw the movie *Black Hawk Down*, you already know the story. However, the movie does not give AC/DC the credit they deserve. When the other Marines searched for their comrade, they wanted him to know that they would not stop searching until he was brought back home.

So they played "Hells Bells," his favorite song, as loudly as possible. Durant remembers, "When you're in captivity if you hear an aircraft, it obviously gets your attention… It was an incredible moment. They had loudspeakers attached to this Black Hawk, flying around the city, broadcasting this music." Finally, after 11 days in captivity, Mike was released.

16. C- Vodka. The memoir written by Bonn's ex-wife, Irene Thornton, bears the title *Have A Drink On Me*. Bonn's companion, Holly X, was enraged that the song was included in the album. She says, "The main reason I went was that I felt they were mocking him in a way, especially by including *Have a Drink on Me* on that album. I felt it necessary to say something on Bon's behalf."

17. Possibly true. There have been claims that Bonn wrote several of the songs on *Back in Black* and did not receive credit for them. Bonn's girlfriend Holly X says, "I've questioned a couple of the songs that were on *Back in Black.* I really think Bon wrote those, like "You Shook Me All Night Long." But he didn't get

any credit. As always, quite possibly [he wrote them] in tandem with the Youngs, but they are his ideas. I have one last thing to say about that song: the lyric is chartreuse eyes, not sightless eyes. A memory I have, which is so clear, is that Bon and I were sitting out in the sun behind the Newport Hotel [in Miami], and he turned to me – the sun was on my face – and he suddenly exclaimed, your eyes are chartreuse! I remember this vividly because I had no idea what color chartreuse was and immediately took it to be something bad, like bright pink or some ghastly color. He referred to my eye color by that word many times." For the record, Holly has chartreuse eyes. Honestly, that does make more sense.

18. C- A drug dealer. Brian was inspired by an article he read about a dealer who makes rounds every morning in the London suburbs, kind of like a milkman. The drug in question was diazepam, which is injected. Therefore, shoot to thrill.

19. True. Most famously, the Beastie Boys sampled "Back in Black" for their song "Rock Hard." Unfortunately, the release had to be withdrawn due

to AC/DC's resistance. Beastie Boys members Mike D said, "AC/DC could not get with the sample concept. They were just like, Nothing against you guys, but we just don't endorse sampling. So we told them that we don't endorse people playing guitars."

20. B- Second, behind Guns N' Roses's classic "Welcome to the Jungle." "Dirty Deeds Done Dirt Cheap" came in 31st. Really? No "Hells Bells?" No "Highway to Hell?"

DID YOU KNOW

- The band swears they felt the presence of Bon during the recording of the album. Malcolm said, "We still think Bon's around," he said. As Malcolm explained, "All these emotions were in play when we were recording." Brian says the feeling that Bon was still around in spirit helped him complete the album: "I was a little worried. Like, who am I to try to follow in the footsteps of this great poet? Bon really was a kind of poet. And something happened to me - a good thing."
- Many who grew up at that time credit *Back in Black* with saving rock 'n' roll. Tom Morello of Rage Against the Machine remembers, "disco was huge, and punk and new-wave were ascendant, and along came this AC/DC record which just destroyed everybody. It put hard rock music back on the throne, where it belongs!" Slash agrees. He says, "*Back in Black* saved rock 'n' roll! It was the defining rock record that came during the biggest lull for rock music. It just exploded! AC/DC was always a great

band, totally genuine. But the miracle of the whole thing was that *Back in Black* was just a great new record; it was still AC/DC. We all missed Bon, but we let him go and at the same time welcomed and embraced Brian."

- On the face of it, *Back In Black* is another very fun record. However, it has a dark aspect and serves as a great memorial to Bon Scott. Angus says it was all intentional: "The whole *Back in Black* album was our dedication to Bon. That's why the album cover was pure black and why the album starts with a bell ringing, something somber and different from anything else we'd done. That is the secret of the album's immortality. We meant it. It's real. It's coming from within. That's how that album was made - because of what we'd all gone through. And that emotion on that record - that will be around forever."

- The band got a special bell cast for the opening sequence of the "Hells Bells" song. At first, they tried to get a recording of a specific church bell in England. However, when that didn't come off, they tried to go through stock bell sounds. Nothing sounded right. The band decided to commission a bell, which they would then also take on tour with them. They put in an order with John Taylor Bellfounders to build a solid bronze bell. Then when Malcolm went to pick it up, there was a problem. The owners "had to get rid of the birds in it," laughs Malcolm. Since the bell weighed a good 2,000 pounds, moving it around on tour proved to be a logistical nightmare. After one tour of endless bell-related headaches, AC/DC sensibly replaced it with a lighter fiberglass alternative. However, the awesome bell sound you hear on the record is as real as it gets.

- Angus denies that Bon helped write the songs. He says that Bon was there at the genesis of some of the songs on the album but had no part in crafting the tunes. "Bon never really got the chance. At the time, me and Malcolm were writing songs, which became the songs for *Back in Black*. We were in London in a rehearsal room, and Bon had come down, too. And what used to happen was me, and Malcolm would get together and get a drum kit, and Malcolm would get behind the drums sometimes, and I'd get on the guitar and just tap out a riff. Or other times, Malcolm would get on the guitar, and he'd get me to just knock out a simple beat on the drums. And the other one was 'Have A Drink On Me,' a riff Malcolm was playing around with. So we worked out the intro on that and how the song was gonna go. So he had Bon tapped to do a demo for that. So that was it, really. If you were looking up what Bon had done, it was really just to help us with those demos on the drums. And he even said to us, as we were knocking off in the nighttime, 'Look, we'll hook up next week.' Anyhow, we were working away, and it was on an intro which was actually what became the intro for 'Hells Bells.' So Bon showed up, and Malcolm said, 'Oh, great, Bon. You can get behind the kit.' Because originally, Bon started as a drummer. So Bon got behind the drum kit so we could try and work out this intro, how we wanted to do it. So we sorted that out how we wanted. He'd been working on some lyrics and said, we'll hook up next week, and maybe the three of us can just start going through stuff. But unfortunately, he passed before that."

CHAPTER 6:

FOR THOSE ABOUT TO ROCK

1. True or False: The album *For Those About to Rock (We Salute You)* was AC/DC's first #1 album in the United States.

2. Where was the album *For Those About to Rock (We Salute You)* recorded?

   a. Paris
   b. London
   c. New York
   d. Sydney

3. True or False: The fruitful partnership between the band and Mutt Lange fell apart during the recording of *For Those About to Rock (We Salute You).*

4. Which member of the band got married between the recording of *Back in Black* and *For Those About to Rock (We Salute You)?*

   a. Brian

    b. Angus
    c. Malcolm
    d. Phil

5. What inspired the cannons in the song "For Those About to Rock (We Salute You)?"
    a. A war movie
    b. Tchaikovsky's *1812 Overture*
    c. A trip to a battlefield
    d. A wedding

6. True or False: The band headlined the first-ever Donnington Monsters of Rock Festival in the middle of recording *For Those About to Rock (We Salute You).*

7. Which was the main vice the band fell into during the *For Those About to Rock* Tour?
    a. Groupies
    b. Drugs
    c. Alcohol
    d. Gambling

8. True or False: *For Those About to Rock (We Salute You)* is the only AC/DC album Angus never listens to.

9. Where did the band record their 1983 album *Flick of the Switch*?

    a. London
    b. The Bahamas
    c. Paris
    d. Los Angeles

10. How many top 40 singles came off the *Flick of the Switch* album?

    a. None
    b. One
    c. Two
    d. Three

11. True or False: Drummer Phil Rudd left the band in 1983 to race cars.

12. How many auditions did AC/DC hold before they hired Simon Wright to replace Phil Rudd in 1983?

    a. Over 100
    b. Over 200
    c. Over 300
    d. Over 500

13. True or False: Even though *Flick of the Switch* did not sell very well, the band has always defended it.

14. True or False: The band produced both *Flick of the Switch* and *Fly on the Wall.*

15. Which guitar shred prodigy played for the opening band on both legs of the Fly on the Wall tour?

    a. Joe Satriani
    b. Eddie Van Halen
    c. Steve Vai
    d. Yngwie Malmsteen

16. The album *Who Made Who* was the soundtrack to a Steven King movie. Which scary movie featured the Australian rockers?

    a. Maximum Overdrive
    b. Firestarter
    c. The Dead Zone
    d. Cujo

17. How many new songs appeared on *Who Made Who*?

    a. None
    b. Two
    c. Three

d. Four

18. Who produced Blow Up Your Video?

    a. The band
    b. Malcolm and Angus
    c. Mutt Lange
    d. Vanda & Young

19. True or False: *Blow Up Your Video* was another commercial failure.

20. Which band member did not tour with AC/DC to support *Blow Up Your Video*?

    a. Angus
    b. Brian
    c. Malcolm
    d. Cliff

ANSWERS

1. True.

2. Paris. The album was recorded at the EMI Pathe-Marconi Studios. The Rolling Stones and Beatles had recorded there previously. However, the band did not like the studio and its acoustics. Mutt, in particular, was unhappy. Engineer Mark Dearnley remembers, "Mutt has a picture of the way he wants to hear it in his head and will keep on bashing away until we hit that particular note that he has," says Dearnley today. "And sometimes it can take some time. They spent the first three days in Paris just on the snare drum sound." They rented the Mobile One Studio and recorded on the outskirts of Paris.

3. True. Everyone involved with that record was unhappy with the result and the process. Therefore, everyone involved proceeded to blame each other. Angus said, "We are always well prepared. We go in the studio with completed songs, and we know what we want. We don't fuck around much - unlike Mutt Lange. But that guy has always been slow. Real slow.

He'd need forever to get anything done. Otherwise, it would have been in and out in a week." Malcolm also said that Mutt "was trying to outdo *Back in Black* for sound, and it was the sound he was looking for whereas we were thinking of the music – and the performances were starting to suffer."

4. B- Angus. Former Whitesnake guitarist Adrian Vandenberg introduced Angus to his wife, Ellen Van Lochem. Adrian's band was warming up AC/DC, and he put Ellen, a friend of his, on the guest list. As Vandenberg recalls, "I put her on the guest list with two friends of hers. Imagine this: Ellen is almost as tall as I am, and I'm six-foot-seven. I think Ellen is probably six-foot-four or something, and we all know Angus is not the tallest guy. I told their bodyguard there's going to be three blondes, very tall chicks coming up in a little bit backstage. Wouldn't it be funny to introduce them to the guys in AC/DC, you know, because they were all pretty short… So he did, and Ellen called me up a couple of weeks later. She was in Paris or something, and a year later, they were married."

5. D- A wedding. Not just any wedding, the royal wedding between Prince Charles and Dianna. A gun salute is part of the traditional reception, and Angus was inspired by it. The guitarist says something clicked for him. He recalls, "I just wanted something strong. Something masculine and rock'n'roll. And what's more masculine than a cannon, you know? I mean, it gets loaded, it fires, and it destroys."
6. False. It was the second iteration of the festival. Rainbow and Judas Priest had headlined the first in 1980. Unfortunately, it was not AC/DC's finest hour. The band was too busy in conflict with Mutt Lange and had not prepared. Brian remembers, "We were shitting ourselves. We thought Fuck, we haven't played this! We haven't rehearsed anything!'" It was a rainy day, and the sound was terrible. Their road manager said, "It was just one of those days. The BBC did something that buggered up the sound that we were getting blamed for. It rained, and the band wasn't really ready for it, even though the date had been in the diary for a long time before. It just sort of

added to all the other things that were going wrong in Paris."

7. Trick question. None of the above. Though the band was now attracting many groupies due to their success, they did not partake. Brian explains that since just about everyone was married, "You never fuck them. You shake hands, and that's it. That's for the crew. They're the ones with the passes, not us." Angus also didn't drink. He explains, "I like a nice cup of tea and a bit of quiet before the show." Cliff and Brian enjoy a few drinks in moderation. The band was living reasonably clean.

8. False. Angus claims to never listen to any of the albums: "I don't listen to any of our albums - ever. I mean, I've written and recorded them. Why would I listen to them?"

9. B- The Bahamas. They returned to Compass Point Studios, where AC/DC had recorded *Back in Black*.

10. C- Two. *Guns for Hire* reached #37, and *Flick of the Switch* reached #26 on the Billboard charts.

11. True. At least according to the official story. Angus said, “We're a rowdy bunch, but we don't fight with each other." And Phil himself said, “I raced cars, flew helicopters, became a farmer, and planted some crops. I lived in New Zealand, which was great; nice and quiet with nobody bothering me." However, it appears that he had a physical altercation with Malcolm that led to his dismissal.

12. D- Over 500. Actually, around 700 auditions. Wright recalls, “I was in London," he said. "I really wasn't doing much. I was in a band in London, but we weren't doing much. Somebody saw an ad in a music paper: Drummer wanted. If you don't hit hard, don't apply.” However, he had no idea it was AC/DC until he had already auditioned for the technical crew and made the second stage. No one told him he was in the band. Instead: “So, we carry on, and the door opens, and I go in and meet them and stuff. It was all very low-key; there was no fanfare as the door opens – they're ready to work. I go in and introduced myself, and they said hello and stuff and everything. They asked me what songs I know, and

I told them a couple, and we got to playing, and we finished up playing for a little while, and they sat down and started talking between themselves and their manager about the upcoming tour and stuff."

13. False. Malcolm has admitted that "It was thrown together real quick. I wouldn't say it's a great album."

14. False. While the entire band produced *Flick of the Switch*, *Fly on the Wall* was produced by Malcolm and Angus to the exclusion of the other members.

15. D- Yngwie Malmsteen. The Swedish guitarist is a known snob who puts down many musicians. However, he has nothing but respect for Angus. Yngwie says, "He's super-tasty and always good! It's still blues, though, even when he does his big solo. Classical isn't just little triplets here and there; it's your entire mind being released from the pentatonic box – a linear kind of playing. And no one really does that."

16. A- *Maximum Overdrive*. King is a big fan of the band and went out of his way to convince the band to participate. When Malcolm died, the writer Tweeted,

"RIP Malcolm Young. Sweet, quiet man. Made all his noise with his guitar. AC/DC night at my house, and loud. Rock and roll ain't noise pollution."

17. C- Three. Two of which were instrumentals. The songs are "D.T.," "Chase the Ace," and the title song.

18. D- Vanda & Young. The use of an outside production team brought some of the missing focus back to their work.

19. False. Although not considered one of their best albums, *Blow Up Your Video* did quite well. It reached #2 in the UK and #12 in the United States. In addition, the single "Heatseeker" carried the album with a good chart showing.

20. C- Malcolm. His alcoholism had gotten entirely out of hand. The band's former agent Doug Thaler remembers, "I'd gone into AC/DC's dressing room and had a scotch with Malcolm and Jonno [Brian Johnson] while Mötley Crüe played. When AC/DC went out to take the stage, Malcolm had clearly had too much to drink. And they were playing the song that Angus used to do his guitar solo and strip to, and Malcolm would just barely keep a steady rhythm—

he couldn't even do that. And he fell into the drum kit, and I thought, oh boy, this is not headed anyplace good." Malcolm knew he had a problem. He admits, "My drinking overtook my whole thing. I felt like Dr. Jekyll and Mr. Hyde. I had a talk with Angus... I was letting people down... I wasn't brain-dead, but I was just physically and mentally screwed by the alcohol."

DID YOU KNOW

- *For Those About to Rock (We Salute You)* is one of the band's best-loved albums. However, the members of AC/DC are not particularly fond of it. Malcolm said, "Christ! It took us forever to make that record, and it sounds like it. It's full of bits and pieces, and it doesn't flow properly like an AC/DC album should... By the time we'd completed it, I don't think anyone ...could tell whether it sounded right or wrong."
- During the recording of *For Those About to Rock (We Salute You)*, the band severed more than one crucial business relationship. Perhaps most importantly, they never worked with Mutt Lange again. Ian Jeffrey, former AC/DC road manager, explained, "It really soured when they started to look at the figures Mutt was being paid. They felt that they didn't need him." Mutt was reportedly very hurt by the decision and refused to discuss it. His one comment was, "Angus has a certain vision for his music, which works for him." They also fired manager Peter

Mensch right after their unsuccessful appearance at Donnington. Mensch was very frustrated because he had just moved to England to be nearer to the band and manage their day-to-day operations. Peter was also very hurt and said, "I was never told why I was fired. They called their lawyer, who called David Krebs, who called me. It was the Thursday after the first Castle Donnington Monsters of Rock show." Jeffrey says, "I think they felt Peter was becoming part of this big thing where the personalized things, the caring, were no longer there. But Peter never stopped caring, believe you me." Considering that the band never did as well commercially again, they may have made a mistake in severing ties with Mensch and Lange. Jeffrey certainly feels it was a mistake. He says, " It was really sad. With Mutt Lange, they were crafted records, without taking away the spontaneity of it sounding like a band playing."

- As the 1980s went on, the Young brothers exerted more and more control over the band's direction. One of the symptoms of this tendency was the removal of Brian Johnson from songwriting duties. The singer wrote all of the lyrics to the *Blow Up Your Video* album. However, after that, he disappeared from the credits. Future albums were credited to the Young brothers. The singer denies that he was cut out of the songwriting cycle. He says he always had trouble coming up with lyrics. He says that even during the recording of *Back in Black,* he suffered from writer's block: "I remember about five songs in, and I was going, gosh darn it, I think I've just ran out of lyrics." He would later explain that he "ran out of words." However, it is clear that the Young brothers wanted more control and to share less of their royalties. However, don't feel bad for Johnson. His net worth is estimated at £50 million.

- AC/DC did not fit in the 1980s musical environment. They did not thrive in a period wherein music videos seemed to become more important than the music. MTV played them occasionally, but it is no coincidence that their album sales plummeted in this image-conscious decade. The title of the album *Blow Up Your Video* is a reference to this fact. Angus explained, “We were probably a band that's best seen in a live situation, and that's how the title came about... 'Cause everything's automatic these days. A kid can flick on the button on a TV, he's got a remote control, and he can zoom through everything and get it coming in from all over the world. You can turn on your radio and get rock coming in from America. For us, the best thing as a band it was always we were great onstage."

CHAPTER 7:

BALANCING ON THE RAZORS EDGE

1. Simon Wright left the band after the *Blow Up Your Video* tour. Which act did he join instead?

    a. Dio
    b. Black Sabbath
    c. Whitesnake
    d. Rainbow

2. AC/DC replaced Simon with drummer Chris Slade. What was Slade's last gig before joining the band?

    a. Uriah Heep
    b. Gary Moore
    c. Manfred Mann
    d. David Gilmour

3. *The Razors Edge* album was recorded in Canada. In which city did they lay down the tracks?

    a. Toronto

b. Ottawa
c. Vancouver
d. Montreal

4. What was the biggest US Billboard single off *The Razors Edge*?

a. "Thunderstruck"
b. "Moneytalks"
c. "Are You Ready"
d. "Rock Your Heart Out"

5. Which member of the band was getting a divorce during the recording of *The Razors Edge*?

a. Brian
b. Malcolm
c. Angus
d. Simon

6. What does the title *The Razors Edge* refer to?

a. Sex
b. Booze
c. Drugs
d. Politics

7. What inspired the song "Thunderstruck?"

a. A drink
b. A toy
c. The weather
d. A kitchen appliance

8. The album *Live* included several recordings from the Monsters of Rock show at Donnington. Which of these songs was NOT recorded at that show?

   a. "Thunderstruck"
   b. "You Shook Me All Night Long"
   c. "The Jack"
   d. "Back in Black"

9. In loving tribute to Bon Scott, the band released the boxed set *Bonfire* in 1997. How many CDs did it include?

   a. Four
   b. Five
   c. Six
   d. Seven

10. True or False: Rick Rubin was hesitant to produce the band on *Ballbreaker*.

11. Which action movie icon was featured in the video for the song "Big Gun?"

    a. Sylvester Stallone
    b. Arnold Schwarzenegger
    c. Bruce Willis
    d. Jean-Claude Van Damme

12. Who inducted the band into the Rock 'N' Roll Hall of Fame?

    a. Steven Tyler
    b. Mick Jagger
    c. Slash
    d. Axl

13. True or False: *Stiff Upper Lip* was produced by the Young & Vanda team again.

14. Brendan O'Brien has produced the most recent albums by the band. Which other major act is O'Brien associated with?

    a. U2
    b. Coldplay
    c. Radiohead
    d. Pearl Jam

15. The band recorded *Power Up* in Vancouver. So which Canadian star owns the studio where they recorded the impressive comeback album?

   a. Shania Twain
   b. Neil Young
   c. Bryan Adams
   d. Celine Dion

16. What is the weirdest place Angus has ever heard AC/DC played?

   a. Antarctica
   b. The Himalayas
   c. A royal coronation
   d. A funeral

17. AC/DC shows are always a bit rowdy. But in one particular show, an audience member used a rocket launcher at the venue. Where did this happen?

   a. Rio de Janeiro
   b. Tokyo
   c. Seattle
   d. Vancouver

18. In 2002, the band signed a massive new recording contract. Which company was lucky enough to obtain the veteran Australian rockers?

    a. Geffen
    b. Columbia
    c. Virgin
    d. Sony

19. In 2000, the band played *Saturday Night Live* for the only time. Who introduced their version of "Stiff Upper Lip" on the show?

    a. Will Smith
    b. Dwayne "the Rock" Johnson
    c. Jennifer Lopez
    d. Harrison Ford

20. True or False: In the book *Under My Thumb: Songs That Hate Women and the Women Who Love Them*, AC/DC are said to be the most misogynistic hard rock band of all time.

ANSWERS

1. A- Dio. Regarding leaving, Simon says, "Basically, it sounds a little crazy, but I really lost my enthusiasm for things. You can't really be like that in a band like that - you've gotta give 110% - and my enthusiasm had become a bit complacent, and it wasn't fair on them, and it definitely wasn't fair on the fans and people coming to the shows." As for why he joined Dio, "I'd met Ronnie a couple of times in the past before that, and I thought he was such a clever, funny, intelligent guy. And I'd loved his singing, obviously, with Sabbath and Rainbow and his own stuff and everything. And it just kind of worked out. Yeah, it was a great time."

2. B- Gary Moore. Incidentally, Chris had played with all of them. The drummer remembers, "I was working with Gary Moore all the way through 1988-89, about a year. They had the same manager, AC/DC, and Gary Moore. His name was Stewart Young, no relation to the Young brothers. I think he put me forward. I think, actually, Malcolm came to a

Gary Moore show in Birmingham." He was one of many drummers who auditioned and thought he had done a terrible job. But, to Slade's surprise, he was offered the job.

3. C- Vancouver. Most of the tracks were recorded at Little Mountain Sound Studio. However, some of the album was made in the Windmill Lane studio in Dublin.

4. B- "Moneytalks." The single reached #3 on the charts. If you were wondering, "Thunderstruck" made #5, and "Are You Ready" made #16. Meanwhile, "Rock Your Heart Out" did not chart.

5. A- Brian. Johnson and his wife Carol had split during the recording of Back in Black as well. They reconciled but finally got divorced during the recording of *The Razors Edge*. That is also part of the explanation for why the singer did not write any of the lyrics for that album. As a result, he was absent when many of the songs were written.

6. D- Politics. AC/DC is not known for its political commentary. However, in this case, they made an

exception. Angus explained, "'The Razors Edge' comes from an old saying farmers used to use in Britain where you'd have a fine sunny day, you know, a very good day with a hot sun, and then all of a sudden right in the distance you could see these black clouds coming over the horizon, an ominous thing...I thought it was a great title. The world was at peace again... and you can see now that it's not that way. It's just our way of saying the world's not perfect and never will be."

7. B- A toy. Namely, the ThunderStreak toy made by the American Ideal Toy Company. It was a hydro wing rubberband-powered toy issued in 1967. Angus says, "We came up with this thunder thing, based on our favorite childhood toy ThunderStreak, and it seemed to have a good ring to it. AC/DC = Power. That's the basic idea."

8. C- "The Jack." That song was recorded at the historic concert in Tushino Airfield, Moscow.

9. B- Five. It includes one CD of early unreleased AC/DC material recorded on 7 December 1977 at the Atlantic Recording Studios. Two CDs comprised

of the soundtrack to the *Let There Be Rock* movie, recorded in Paris in 1979. One CD had rare and unreleased tracks from various sessions. And the final album was a remastered version of *Back in Black.*

10. False. Rubin was a huge fan. Like many producers, he used AC/DC's classic recordings as a benchmark for his production sound. For example, engineer Tony Platt remembers that when they were working together on an album for British band The Cult, "as he was mixing, he was getting a guitar sound on The Cult and then comparing it directly with the guitar sound that he wanted to get from Back in Black. The same with all the other instruments."

11. B- Arnold Schwarzenegger. The song featured on the soundtrack for the movie *Last Action Hero,* and the star appeared in the video. Arnold hilariously put on the schoolboy uniform and imitated the Angus walk. Director David Mallet remembers, "I remember standing behind the set with Arnold Schwarzenegger trying to teach him to do the Angus walk. And the

crew were filming me imitating Angus's walk, and that was a real laugh."

12. A- Steven Tyler. Steven had always been a fan and had supported AC/DC in getting their big break in the United States. Malcolm remembers, "We were on a gig with Foreigner, who had a big hit record at the time, and it was a big stadium. Aerosmith was on it, too. Foreigner didn't want us on there for one reason or another, and it was Steven Tyler who said, well, if you're gonna drop them, we're not playing either. I thought that was brilliant. So when we look back, we thought he was the man who helped the band when we first came to the States, and we're grateful for that."

13. False. George Young produced it without his long-time musical partner Harry Vanda. Brian, for one, was happy to work with George. The singer commented that "In the past, he's always worked with Harry. Not detracting from Harry, but it was kinda streamlined this time. You had no one to answer to or discuss things with except Malcolm or Angus. We were working pretty hard this time

actually, from about 11 in the morning until one the next morning sometimes. Saturdays as well. It was good, though. George always had a game plan. I hate it when you're hanging around waiting for the next decision. George always had it all worked out."

14. D- Pearl Jam. Brendan pushed the band in a different direction. He wanted them to be more melodic. Brendan says, "The AC/DC music that I remember most is "Highway To Hell" and "Back in Black," which I view as pop songs done in a very heavy, ferocious way. Angus and Malcolm were writing songs that had a lot of hooks, and my only job was to make a record that made people say: I've missed AC/DC, and I'm glad they're back."

15. C- Bryan Adams.

16. B- The Himalayas. Angus says, "up there in Nepal. There were people there who loved us, and some people even told me that they have a cover band that covers a lot of what we do, way up in the Himalayas."

17. C- Seattle. Angus remembers, "in Seattle once, when somebody fired a rocket launcher into the dome, the roof of where we were playing—I think it was the Tacoma Dome. But the roof caught on fire, and I could see smoke, smoke all around me... but they managed to get the fire out, and then we got back on stage and finished the show."

18. D- Sony. The deal included future recordings. However, just as importantly, it allowed Sony rights to reissue AC/DC's back catalog.

19. B- Dwayne "the Rock" Johnson. The band also played "You Shook Me All Night Long."

20. False. The book is critical of the band's lyrics, calling them "a bunch of archly sex-obsessed idiots with sharp tunes and some seriously killer riffs." But writer Fiona Sturges also notes that in songs like "Whole Lotta Rosie" and "You Shook Me All Night Long," the female characters are "also having a good time and are, more often than not, in the driving seat in sexual terms... it's the men who come over as passive and hopeless, awestruck in the presence of

sexual partners more experienced and adept than them."

DID YOU KNOW

- Three fans were killed in AC/DC's show in Salt Lake City, held in January 1991. The band started its opening song, "Thunderstruck," and the fans rushed the stage. Unfortunately, there was a brutal race with no assigned seating to take the best spots up front amongst the 13,000 fans in attendance. The band was horrified. Brian Johnson remembers, "Terrible night. I'll never forget it for as long as I live. I was shattered. Angus was beside himself. I could see he was welling up. Mal was trying to hold it together as best he could." So the band played on for a while, unaware of what had happened. Once the magnitude of the disaster was clear, the local authorities asked the band to complete the set to avoid rioting. Unfortunately, the press reported the sequence of events unfairly. Brian recalls, "I think what hurt most was, the next day in the newspapers they were saying the band played on while kids died about them and they had a photograph of me with a smile on my face. It was just journalistic opportunism that went beyond the bounds of decency. I was so angry and hurt." A series of lawsuits regarding these events were settled out of court for undisclosed sums of money.

- AC/DC made more positive history in 1991 by playing the first outdoor rock festival in Moscow following the disintegration of the Soviet Union. Reportedly 1.5 million people attended the historic Monsters of Rock event. Pantera and Metallica headlined the show alongside the Australian band. The show was not planned and was thrown together at the last minute. There had just been a failed coup attempt against the Boris Yeltsin-led government in the Kremlin. President Yeltsin asked the Monsters of Rock organizers to bring the show to Moscow to cement the change in the country. Brian remembers, "One show that stands out main memory more than anything was that time we shared a stage in Moscow - and we were in Barcelona - we got the call from Yeltsin. Well, not him personally, but it said, 'You must come up to Moscow because the coup is over, and we promised the kids.' They wanted rock 'n' roll." The singer almost got shot by Soviet soldiers for peeing on the Sputnik satellite. I went out the back, and there was a concrete column with an old rusty ball on, and I remember thinking just, I'll take a pee here. And the two soldiers came up with a rifle; they were gonna shoot me. And I didn't realize it was Sputnik, and it was quite a revered thing. But you could see in an instant how cruel and brutal these guys were."

- Phil Rudd returned to the band in 1993. The band had asked him to jam with them in 1991 casually, and two years later, they made it official. The band decided to fire Chris Slade seem amicable, but Chris feels he was mistreated. Slade had already demoed parts for all of the songs on the *Ballbreaker* album, and Rudd was brought in to just record all of his parts with very minimal changes. Chris claims that the band tried to keep him on while they figured out if Rudd could still play or not. However, Slade refused to remain as a backup. He recalls telling Malcolm, "Well, I'm gone, and if he can't play drums, that's your problem now, Malcolm."

Following that incident, Slade did not play for quite a while: "After that, I didn't touch a drumstick for three years. It just knocked me back. I thought you do your best - as I always do, as I always have - and it's not appreciated, and I thought, I've had enough of this business."

CHAPTER 8:

LOSING MALCOLM AND CARRYING ON

1. In 2016, Brian Johnson stepped aside, and Axl Rose toured with the band instead. Why didn't Brian tour with AC/DC?

    a. He decided to retire.
    b. A dispute over royalties
    c. The band wanted a change.
    d. Health problems

2. In 2016, Cliff Williams retired from music and left AC/DC. Where did he play his last show with the band?

    a. Philadelphia
    b. Atlanta
    c. Detroit
    d. Phoenix

3. True or False: Angus and Malcolm refused to let their music be used for video games.
4. Which of AC/DC's recent albums is the longest-running LP in their discography?
   a. Stiff Upper Lip
   b. Black Ice
   c. Rock or Bust
   d. Power Up
5. True or False: The band had the highest-selling album of 2008.
6. Which song on *Black Ice* saw Angus play a slide guitar lead?
   a. "Rock N Roll Train"
   b. "Skies on Fire"
   c. "Stormy May Day"
   d. "Decibel"
7. True or False: *Black Ice* was the most downloaded album on iTunes in 2008.
8. Which member of the band was placed on house arrest during the recording of *Rock or Bust*?

a. Angus
b. Brian
c. Phil
d. Cliff

9. Malcolm had to step aside before the recording of *Rock or Bust*. Stevie Young on rhythm guitar replaced him. How is Stevie related to Malcolm?

   a. He is his son.
   b. He is his cousin.
   c. He is his grandson.
   d. He is his nephew.

10. *Rock or Bust* was the first record the band made without Malcolm. Who wrote the songs on the album?

    a. Angus & Malcolm
    b. Angus
    c. The whole band
    d. Angus & Stevie

11. In 2015, AC/DC launched its first beer. Which German company released the Australian rocker take on lager?

a. Beck's
b. Paulaner
c. Karlsberg
d. Erdinger

12. True or False: When Brian Johnson experienced the worst of his hearing trouble, he was replaced by Axl Rose. But, unfortunately, the two big egos of Angus and Axl did not get along.

13. True or False: In 2018, the band announced that Phil, Cliff, and Brian were re-joining the band for a new album before starting new sessions.

14. The band's big comeback single, "Shot in the Dark," was used as a theme song for a major sporting event. Which event adopted the song?

    a. The NFL All-Star Game
    b. The WWE Survivor Series
    c. The NCAA Final-Four
    d. UFC Fight Night

15. True or False: Angus wanted to include Malcolm's guitar playing on *Rock or Bust* but couldn't find high-quality takes.

16. Which car company signed a deal with AC/DC to promote their new model using their new music?

    a. Chevrolet
    b. Ford
    c. Dodge
    d. Cadillac

17. How many drummers have AC/DC had in their history?

    a. Five
    b. Six
    c. Seven
    d. Eight

18. *Back in Black* is the band's highest-selling album. What was the second highest?

    a. Highway to Hell
    b. The Razors Edge
    c. AC/DC Live
    d. For Those About to Rock

19. How many Grammys did AC/DC win?

    a. None
    b. One

c. Five

d. Ten

20. How many AC/DC albums have reached #1 in the Billboard album charts?

    a. Three
    b. Five
    c. Seven
    d. Nine

ANSWERS

1. D- Health problems. Namely, Brian was losing his hearing. However, he worked with an expert and figured out a method whereby the singer could go back on the road with the band. Johnson remembers. An expert had invented a form of earphones that made it possible. Johnson recalls, "it worked straight away... I don't have the words. I really don't have the words to tell you how I felt. But I know 'happy' was one of them. It was really good."

2. A- Philadelphia. Cliff stated that "It's been what I've known for the past 40 years, but after this tour, I'm backing off of touring and recording. Losing Malcolm, the thing with Phil, and now with Brian, it's a changed animal. I feel in my gut it's the right thing."

3. False. The band has had material appear more than once on the *Rock Band* game. First, "Let There Be Rock" was included on Rock Band 2. Then they released *AC/DC Live: Rock Band Track Pack through* Walmart. It includes playable versions of most of

their big hits. However, the band did not allow the use of their images, much to the disappointment of long-time fans.

4. B- *Black Ice*. The album clocks in at 55 minutes and 37 seconds.

5. False. But almost true. *Black Ice* was second only to Coldplay's *Viva La Vida* or *Death and All His Friends,* selling six million copies in 2008.

6. C- "Stormy May Day." It was Brendan O'Brien's idea. It was part of his attempt to push the band to do things they were less comfortable with. Angus remembers, "It gives you a bit of a kick up the butt. The guy's not gonna let just anything cruise; he'll make you work."

7. False. The band refused to allow the album onto the then popular platform. Brian explains, "We're the only band left in the world now that hasn't signed to iTunes. We want people to buy a record, a physical thing, not a number on a fucking download, which is what it's turning into." However, in 2012 they caved and put their work on the service.

8. C- Phil. Drummer Phil Rudd was arrested in 2015 for threatening to kill a former co-worker. He was confined to house arrest in his New Zealand home. He was also sentenced for possession of marijuana and amphetamines. There were also plans to prosecute Rudd for attempting to hire an assassin, but they were dropped due to a lack of evidence. The band fired him soon after.

9. B- He is his cousin. Stevie had filled in for Malcolm before, in the 1980s, when the rhythm guitarist was struggling with alcoholism. Angus says his style of play is very similar: "Stevie always played like Malcolm. He grew up on it, and that was who he emulated. He copied it. So he's doing great."

10. A- Angus & Malcolm. They had quite a few old songs kicking around. Angus explained, "We'd had quite a long break in between *Black Ice* and the album previous, so there were a lot of years where me and Malcolm just worked on song ideas for AC/DC together."

11. C- Karlsberg. Not to be confused with the Danish Carlsberg, released AC/DC Rock or Bust, a beer brewed to the band's specifications.

12. False. Axl is famous for being hard to work with. However, he has matured in recent years. That has allowed Guns N' Roses to reform and helped him fill in for Brian Johnson quite smoothly. Angus says, "I'd heard a lot of things, but I talked to him one-on-one, and he was very respectful to me and the others…If we were there to do the show, he was there, and he was there at the same time as us, ready to go."

13. False. They weren't sure it would work out, so the band met in Vancouver in secret during 2018. Brian says, "We wanted to do it in secret in case nothing came of it," Johnson recalls, "and of course somebody took photographs when we were having a sneaky cigarette on the fire steps outside the studio."

14. B- The WWE Survivor Series. It is a popular pay-per-view wrestling event.

15. False. There were plenty of tapes of Malcolm lying around, but Angus chose not to use them. Angus explained, "I chose consciously not to do that. Malcolm was his own unique style, and I didn't want to start chopping up pieces. I know they have the tools these days to do it, but he wouldn't be a fan of that. He would want it to be one solid take. And being his brother, I would feel a bit strange doing that way."
16. C- Dodge. The 60-minute commercial featured "Shot in the Dark" and has several Dodge vehicles in it.
17. D- Eight. Aside from current drummer Phil Rudd, they include Colin Burgess, Ron Carpenter, Russell Coleman, Noel Taylor, Peter Clack, Simon Wright, and Chris Slade.
18. A- *Highway to Hell.* The classic Bon Scott fronted album sold 7 million copies worldwide and counting.
19. B- One. In 2010 they won Best Hard Rock Performance for the song "War Machine."

20. A- Three, and probably not the three you have in mind. The #1 albums are *For Those About to Rock (We Salute You)*, *Black Ice*, and *Power Up*.

DID YOU KNOW?

- Malcolm was diagnosed with dementia and underwent a long and painful decline. It was an incredibly difficult and emotional process for Angus. But, he told Australian TV, I think the hardest part was not so much him passing, because that was a kind of end, a relief. I think the worst part is the decline – that's the hard part. Because of how you knew him, and then to see that that was gone." The two also maintained a strong connection right until the end. "I would say, even to the end, if I was there, he had a big smile. And for me, that always gave me a kind of joy. Even though he was in that state, that was always the joy of it. And he still got a great kick if I played him guitar. He would try to tap his foot. But he always knew I was there. So that was a big thing. I was with him towards the end."

- Brian Johnson is not particularly confident in his singing abilities. As the English singer has gotten older, the problem has gotten worse. He says, "I'm not a great singer," he admitted, "but I'm a passionate singer. I've gotta have a mic in me hand, and I have to be able to move, which you can't do when there's a static mic. I think you've been able to tell on the last couple of albums; it's just been getting almost mechanical. And I wasn't proud of it." When recording the *Black Ice* album, he remembers telling producer Brendan O'Brien, "Brendan, if I'm not up to scratch, if I'm not up to the job, please, please tell me. I'm a big boy. I won't cry; I'll just disappear. I'll say goodbye to the boys, and they can get someone else in to do the job. And I really mean it." But O'Brien helped Johnson recapture his confidence. The results are there for all to hear. Johnson is singing better than ever. Brian remembers that when he listened to the playbacks for Black Ice: "I thought I was listening to meself when I was a young man. And I can only put that down to Brendan O'Brien."

- Angus has always been the star of the band. But Malcolm was, without a doubt, its leader. Jeffrey explained, "They would discuss things between them, but Malcolm was the decision-maker. Bon was his own man, but the band belonged to Malcolm. It was Malcolm who told Phil Rudd to stick to the beat; Malcolm who told Cliff where to stand and when to come to the mic. When Brian joined, it was Malcolm that told him to shut the fuck up between songs and just stand there and sing. It would always be Malcolm, every direction or turning they took." Former drummer Simon Wright agrees and adds, "He was definitely in control of things. He could change situations around with a couple of words and couple of suggestions. He was quite a leader and such a fantastic guitar player, too." Brian summed up what everyone in the band feels about Malcolm: "Even though Malcolm is no longer with us, he was a strong character in life, and he [still] hasn't given up, let's put it that way. We're not spiritualists or anything, but he's there."

We hope you enjoyed our journey into the life and times of AC/DC. When you delve into the trials and tribulations this band has been through, their tenacity and consistency are all the more remarkable. And keep in mind, there is still more to come. Their last album, *Power Up*, reached number one in every significant chart in the world. The relentless and joyous noise AC/DC creates is going nowhere. And it is not, nor has it ever been noise pollution.

Printed in the USA
CPSIA information can be obtained
at www.ICGtesting.com
LVHW020254170923
758379LV00013B/383

9 781955 149273